Limerick County Library

30012 00656128 5

KU-342-404

WITHDRAWN FROM STOCK

GRAP
ASTRONAUTS

by David West

illustrated by Jim Robins

W
FRANKLIN WATTS
LONDON•SYDNEY

Limerick
County Library

00656128

First published in 2010 by Franklin Watts

Franklin Watts
338 Euston Road
London NW1 3BH

Franklin Watts Australia
Level 17/207 Kent Street
Sydney, NSW 2000

All rights reserved.

A CIP catalogue record for this book is available from the British Library.

Dewey number: 629.4'5

ISBN: 978 0 7496 9253 7
Franklin Watts is a division of Hachette Children's Books, an Hachette UK company.
www.hachette.co.uk

GRAPHIC CAREERS: ASTRONAUTS produced for Franklin Watts by David West
Children's Books, 7 Princeton Court, 55 Felsham Road, London SW15 1AZ

Copyright © 2008 David West Children's Books

Designed and produced by
David West Children's Books

Editor: Gail Bushnell

Photo credits: All photographs on pages 4–7 and 44–45 by NASA.

Printed in China

Website disclaimer:
Note to parents and teachers: Every effort has been made by the Publishers to ensure
that the websites in this book are suitable for children, that they are of the highest
educational value, and that they contain no inappropriate or offensive material.
However, because of the nature of the Internet, it is impossible to guarantee that the
contents of these sites will not be altered. We strongly advise that Internet access is
supervised by a responsible adult.

CONTENTS

LIVING AND WORKING IN SPACE

Manned space stations have been orbiting the Earth since 1971. The early Russian space station programme, called Salyut, carried out research into living in space and paved the way for the later multimodular space stations, such as Mir and the International Space Station (ISS).

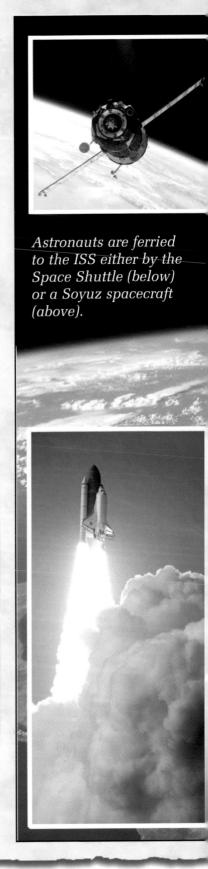

Astronauts are ferried to the ISS either by the Space Shuttle (below) or a Soyuz spacecraft (above).

LIVING AND WORKING IN WEIGHTLESSNESS

Astronauts on board the ISS continue to research the effects of long-term space flight on the human body. They also carry out scientific studies and experiments.

The duration record of 437.7 days was set by Valeriy Polyakov aboard Mir (above) from 1994 to 1995. The station existed until 23 March 2001, at which time it was deliberately deorbited, breaking apart during atmospheric reentry over the South Pacific Ocean.

Living and working in space brings a unique set of problems. Regular exercise is a must to keep muscles and bones from degenerating (1). Because there is no gravity to keep things on the floor or tabletop, everything has to be strapped or Velcroed down. This includes astronauts when they are sleeping (2). Food crumbs and moisture must not get into the electronics, so care has to be taken with the specially prepared food and drink packs (3).

The ISS is continually being added to, which requires astronauts to work in space wearing space suits.

The ISS is in low Earth orbit and can be seen from Earth by the naked eye. It orbits approximately 330 kilometres above the Earth. It has been continually inhabited since 2 November 2000 and so far has been visited by astronauts from 14 countries.

ASTRONAUT TRAINING

An astronaut may be a commander/pilot, mission specialist or payload specialist.

ASTRONAUTS

Commander/pilots fly the Shuttle and may deploy satellites using the Shuttle's mechanical arm. Training includes flying Shuttle simulators and Shuttle training aircraft. Mission specialists have a specific job to do, such as a spacewalk to attach a new part to the ISS. Training requires hundreds of hours in the Neutral Buoyancy Laboratory (NBL), a large water tank that simulates weightlessness, and on computer simulators and virtual reality programmes. The payload specialist performs any specialised duties the mission requires. Payload specialists are people other than NASA personnel and some are foreign nationals.

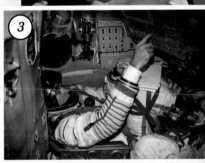

1. Mission specialist using virtual reality hardware in the Space Vehicle Mockup Facility. 2. Testing an Extravehicular Mobility Unit (EMU) space suit on board a KC-135 aircraft, which provides weightlessness for 20 seconds at a time. 3. An astronaut at the Russian space programme on a Soyuz simulator. 4. The Space Shuttle cockpit simulator. 5. Astronauts practise landings in the KC-135 as it is similar in gross weight to a Shuttle. 6. Training on the motion-based Shuttle simulator. 7. Canadian D. Williams during mission specialist training in the NBL.

Yuri Alexeyevich Gagarin

COSMONAUT

The First Person in Space

12 APRIL 1961, SOUTHWEST OF ENGELS SMELOVKA, SARATOV, USSR*. A YOUNG GIRL RUNS SCREAMING TO HER MOTHER, WHO WATCHES AN APPROACHING FIGURE IN STRANGE CLOTHING.

DON'T BE AFRAID. I AM A SOVIET, A FRIEND.

I MUST FIND A TELEPHONE TO CALL MOSCOW.

*UNION OF SOVIET SOCIALIST REPUBLICS.

THREE HOURS EARLIER (8:00 AM). YURI GAGARIN IS STRAPPED INTO THE SPACE CAPSULE, VOSTOK 1, WHISTLING SOFTLY.

VOSTOK 1 IS TO BE CONTROLLED FROM THE BUNKER. THERE IS A SECRET CODE TO UNLOCK THE FLIGHT CONTROLS FOR MANUAL CONTROL. THIS WILL BE GIVEN TO GAGARIN ONLY IN AN EMERGENCY.

IT IS TIME FOR IVANOVSKY TO CLOSE AND SEAL THE HATCH. HE FEELS IT IS WRONG TO KEEP THE CODE FROM GAGARIN.

YURI, THE CODE NUMBERS ARE...

YES, I KNOW. KOROLEV TOLD ME AND KAMININ. THANK YOU ANYWAY.

10

THE HATCH IS REATTACHED WITH NO PROBLEMS. KOROLEV GIVES THE ORDER FOR LAUNCH.

20 SECONDS INTO THE FLIGHT.

I AM ZARYA-1. WE ARE ALL WISHING YOU A GOOD FLIGHT. IS EVERYTHING OK?

THANK YOU. BYE-BYE. SEE YOU SOON, DEAR FRIENDS.

IGNITION IS BEING GIVEN, KEDR. I AM ZARYA-1.

AT 9:07 AM MOSCOW TIME, THE R-7 ROCKET CARRYING VOSTOK 1 LIFTS OFF.

COMPLETE TAKEOFF.

LET'S GO!

TWO MINUTES INTO THE FLIGHT, THE ROCKET BOOSTERS FALL AWAY.

THREE MINUTES INTO THE FLIGHT THE NOSE CONE FALLS AWAY, AS EXPECTED.

KEDR. I CAN SEE THE EARTH. VISIBILITY IS FINE.

THE PRESSURE OF G-FORCES BEGINS TO PRESS GAGARIN BACK INTO HIS SEAT.

I AM ZARYA-1. HOW ARE YOU FEELING? I AM ZARYA – OVER.

I AM KEDR. I AM FEELING FINE.

SUDDENLY, THERE IS A SICKENING JOLT. VOSTOK STARTS SPINNNG.

THIS IS NOT RIGHT.

THE INSTRUMENT MODULE, INSTEAD OF SEPARATING FROM THE DESCENT CAPSULE, IS STILL ATTACHED BY SOME CABLES.

AS THE TWO PARTS SPIN AROUND EACH OTHER, THE G-FORCES THREATEN TO CAUSE GAGARIN TO BLACK OUT.

GNNN. MUST... STAY... CONSCIOUS.

THE CAPSULE GETS HOTTER AND HOTTER AS THE FRICTION OF THE AIR OVER THE CAPSULE BURNS THE OUTER LAYERS.

AT 10:35 AM THE CABLES HOLDING THE TWO PARTS BURN AWAY AND THEY SEPARATE. THERE ARE STILL 20 MINUTES OF DESCENT TO GO AS GAGARIN ENDURES EIGHT G'S.

AT 10:55 AM THERE IS A LOUD EXPLOSION AS THE ESCAPE HATCH IS EJECTED AT SEVEN KILOMETRES ABOVE THE EARTH.

BLAM

SECONDS LATER, GAGARIN IS BLASTED FROM THE CAPSULE IN HIS EJECTOR SEAT.

LOOK, MAMA. WHAT IS IT?

AS HE BEGINS TO FALL, HIS PARACHUTE OPENS AND HIS SEAT FALLS AWAY. AT THE SAME TIME THE CAPSULE'S PARACHUTE OPENS AND BOTH MAN AND MACHINE FLOAT DOWN TO EARTH.

THE END

DR. JERRY LINENGER
ASTRONAUT
FIRE IN SPACE

24 FEBRUARY 1997. AMERICAN ASTRONAUT JERRY LINENGER HAS BEEN ON THE RUSSIAN SPACE STATION, MIR, FOR FIVE WEEKS WITH COSMONAUTS VALERI KORZUN AND ALEXANDER KALERI. TWO WEEKS EARLIER, A RUSSIAN REPLACEMENT TEAM OF VASILY TSIBLIEV, ALEXANDER LAZUTKIN AND GERMAN RESEARCHER REINHOLD EWALD HAD ARRIVED IN A SOYUZ CAPSULE.

THERE WAS A 20-DAY OVERLAP BEFORE THE OLD CREW RETURNED TO EARTH. THE SPACE STATION WAS CRAMPED WITH THE SIX OF THEM AND IT PUT A STRAIN ON THE OXYGEN SUPPLY.

LINENGER LEAVES THE DINNER TABLE TO CHECK SOME DATA IN THE SPEKTR MODULE. LAZUTKIN HEADS OFF TO A TUNNEL CONNECTING THE BASE BLOCK TO THE KVANT 1 MODULE TO ACTIVATE AN OXYGEN CANISTER.*

EXCUSE ME. I'M JUST GOING TO CHECK ON SOME RESULTS.

*SMALL, WASTEBASKET-SIZE CYLINDRICAL CANISTERS FILLED WITH A CHEMICAL SLURRY THAT, WHEN ACTIVATED, RELEASE OXYGEN.

BLAAANG   BLAAANG   BLAAANG

SUDDENLY THE FIRE ALARM GOES OFF.

IT IS ALMOST A DAILY OCCURRENCE AND LINENGER IS NOT WORRIED.

I BET THE CARBON DIOXIDE SCRUBBERS HAVE FAILED AGAIN.

00656128

Limerick
County Library

FINDING ONE, HE RIPS IT OFF THE WALL, QUICKLY PUTS THE MASK OVER HIS FACE, AND SWITCHES ON THE AIRFLOW.

IT DOESN'T WORK!

DESPERATE FOR AIR, LINENGER GROPES HIS WAY THROUGH THE THICK SMOKE.

OPEN A WINDOW! NO, THAT'S ABSURD!

HE FEELS THE BULGE OF A RESPIRATOR CASE. RIPPING IT OPEN, HE PULLS THE MASK TO HIS FACE AND SWITCHES ON THE AIR.

AHHHHHH, I CAN BREATHE.

AFTER A MINUTE HE STRAPS THE MASK ON PROPERLY AND MEETS THE OTHERS AT THE MAIN NODE.

LINENGER AND KORZUN HEAD TOWARDS THE FIRE WITH A FIRE EXTINGUISHER, WHILE THE OTHERS PREPARE A SOYUZ CAPSULE FOR EVACUATION.

THERE'S ONLY ROOM FOR THREE PEOPLE IN THE SOYUZ. WE MUST PUT OUT THIS FIRE.

LINENGER HOLDS ON TO KORZUN WHILE HE USES THE FIRE EXTINGUISHER.

IT'S NOT MAKING ANY DIFFERENCE.

AFTER USING THREE FIRE EXTINGUISHERS, THE FIRE TAKES FOURTEEN MINUTES TO BURN OUT.

THE FIRE IS OUT!

THE SMOKE LINGERS IN THE STATION FOR SOME TIME. IT TAKES A WHILE BEFORE IT BECOMES SAFE TO BREATHE THE AIR. LINENGER TREATS SOME CREW MEMBERS WITH MINOR BURNS, BUT THERE ARE NO SERIOUS INJURIES. LINENGER STAYED ON MIR FOR 132 DAYS AND WAS PICKED UP BY ATLANTIS IN MAY 1997. **THE END**

THOMAS D. JONES
——ASTRONAUT——
SPACE SHUTTLE MISSION STS-98

AUGUST 2000. THE CREW OF STS-98 ARE: COMMANDER KENNETH D. 'TACO' COCKRELL, PILOT MARK L.'ROMAN' POLANSKI, AND MISSION SPECIALISTS ROBERT L. 'BEAMER' CURBEAM, MARSHA S. IVINS AND THOMAS D. JONES.

TWO IMUS* ARE DOWN! OH, HECK, THERE GOES THE LAST ONE!

50,000 FEET, ONE POINT TWO G'S.

*INERTIAL MEASURING UNITS. WITHOUT AT LEAST ONE OF THESE OPERATING, THE SHUTTLE ORBITER CANNOT CONTROL ITS GLIDE BACK TO EARTH.

AS MISSION CONTROL ADVISES THE CREW, THE SHUTTLE COMMANDER, KENNETH 'TACO' COCKRELL, HITS THE BFS* BUTTON.

ATLANTIS, ENGAGE BFS.

*BACKUP FLIGHT SYSTEM.

EVERYBODY HEAVES A SIGH OF RELIEF AS THE THIRD IMU STARTS TO OPERATE AGAIN.

PHEW!

SUDDENLY, THE ORBITER ROLLS VIOLENTLY...

WHOA!

WE'RE ALL DEAD...

...OR WOULD BE IF IT WASN'T A SIMULATION.

WHAT WENT WRONG?

TOM LOOKS AT HIS CHECKLIST AND SEES THE PROBLEM.

WE MISSED A PROCEDURE AFTER THE BFS ENGAGE.

IT SEEMS WE STILL HAVE PLENTY OF WORK TO DO.

MARSHA IVINS HAS ONE OF THE MOST DIFFICULT JOBS. SHE HAS TO MOVE THE NEW DESTINY LAB FROM THE CARGO BAY TO THE INTERNATIONAL SPACE STATION (ISS) USING THE SHUTTLE'S ROBOT ARM.

I'VE GOT TO GET THIS RIGHT. THERE'S ONLY TWO INCHES ON EITHER SIDE BETWEEN THE LAB AND THE CARGO BAY WALLS.

AS MISSION SPECIALISTS, ROBERT CURBEAM AND TOM SPEND HUNDREDS OF HOURS IN THE NEUTRAL BUOYANCY LABORATORY (NBL). THEY ARE TRAINING FOR THE THREE SPACE WALKS WHEN THEY WILL ATTACH THE NEW DESTINY LAB TO THE ISS.

THE SPACE WALKS WILL LAST SIX HOURS EACH, SO THERE IS PLENTY OF TRAINING TO GET THROUGH. IT IS HARD, DEMANDING WORK.

NOT ALL THE TRAINING IS HARD WORK. ROBERT AND TOM HAVE CLASSES IN THE VIRTUAL REALITY LAB. HERE, THEY PUT ON A PAIR OF 3-D TELEVISION GOGGLES AND PRACTISE USING THE NITROGEN-POWERED JET PACK. THIS IS IN CASE THE TETHERS BREAK AND THEY FLOAT OFF INTO SPACE.

'YOU ARE TOSSED OFF THE ISS, TUMBLING HEAD OVER HEELS...'

'FIRST YOU STOP YOURSELF FROM TUMBLING...'

'THEN YOU ROTATE UNTIL YOU SEE THE ISS...'

'FINALLY, YOU THRUST YOURSELF TOWARDS THE STATION.'

WHILE THE CREW OF STS-98 CONTINUES TRAINING, THE FIRST CREW TO TAKE UP RESIDENCE IN THE ISS ARRIVES AT THE BEGINNING OF NOVEMBER 2000. THEY ARE BILL SHEPHERD, SERGEI KRIKALEV AND YURI GIDZENKO.

ON 2 DECEMBER 2000, ENDEAVOUR DOCKS WITH THE ISS AND ERECTS THE P6 TRUSS WITH A PAIR OF SOLAR ARRAYS. STS-98'S TURN IS NEXT...

AFTER LONG DELAYS, THE DATE FOR LAUNCH IS FEBRUARY 2001, AT KENNEDY SPACE CENTER (KSC). THE CREW ENTERS QUARANTINE ON 31 JANUARY. THIS KEEPS THEM AWAY FROM DAY-TO-DAY ENCOUNTERS WITH COLLEAGUES AND FAMILY THAT MIGHT EXPOSE THEM TO INFECTION.

ON 4 FEBRUARY, THE CREW FLIES TO KSC, WHERE THEIR FAMILIES ARE WAITING.

THE CREW AND THEIR FAMILIES ARE ALLOWED TO LOOK OVER ATLANTIS.

THREE DAYS LATER, THE CREW MEMBERS ARE ALL STRAPPED IN, READY FOR TAKEOFF. TOM IS ALONE ON THE MID DECK. ON THE RETURN TRIP, HE WILL SIT ON THE UPPER DECK WITH THE REST OF THE CREW.

OK, TOM, YOU'RE GOOD TO GO.

THANKS, RAY J, I'LL SEE YOU IN A COUPLE OF WEEKS.

GREG 'RAY J' JOHNSON AND THE REST OF THE 'CLOSE-OUT CREW' LEAVE THE CABIN AND CLOSE THE ORBITER HATCH.

TIME TO TAKE MY ANTINAUSEA PILL.

THE CALM VOICES OF THE LAUNCH TEAM GO THROUGH THE COUNTDOWN LIST.

T-MINUS-60 MINUTES...

5:53 PM.

WE ARE GOOD TO PROCEED.

COPY THAT. THE CREW THANKS THE KSC TEAM. LET'S GET THIS VEHICLE OFF THE LAUNCH PAD.

T-MINUS-NINE MINUTES AND COUNTING. GLS* HAS BEEN INITIATED.

*GROUND LAUNCH SEQUENCER.

THE GANTRY SWING ARM RETRACTS.

PLT*, PERFORM APU* START-UP.

*PLT = SHUTTLE PILOT.
*APU = AUXILIARY POWER UNITS.

APU START COMPLETE.

THREE MINUTES AND COUNTING.

ALL FLIGHT CREW, CLOSE AND LOCK YOUR VISORS AND START OXYGEN FLOW.

A LEVER ON THE SUIT SWITCHES ON THE OXYGEN.

CLICK

TEN SECONDS...

GO FOR MAIN ENGINE START.

RUMBLE

BOOM

JUST AFTER THE THREE MAIN ENGINES FIRE, THE TWO SOLID ROCKET BOOSTERS (SRBS) FIRE.

AS THE SHUTTLE ACCELERATES, THE CREW IS SUBJECTED TO TWO AND A HALF G'S. THE ACCELERATION LESSENS AS THE TWO SRBS RUN OUT OF FUEL.

SEVEN MINUTES INTO THE FLIGHT, AND ATLANTIS IS TRAVELLING AT 19 TIMES THE SPEED OF SOUND, SUBJECTING THE CREW TO OVER THREE G'S.

HEY, THERE'S A GORILLA SITTING ON MY CHEST!

BANG

EXPLOSIVE BOLTS SHEAR THE TWO SRBS FROM THE EXTERNAL FUEL TANK.

CLANG

PARACHUTES SLOW THEIR DESCENT TO THE OCEAN, WHERE THEY WILL BE PICKED UP TO BE REUSED ON A FUTURE SHUTTLE MISSION.

AT EIGHT MINUTES INTO THE FLIGHT, THE MAIN ENGINES ARE CUT OFF AND ATLANTIS ROLLS 180 DEGREES. TEN SECONDS LATER, THE EXTERNAL FUEL TANK IS RELEASED WITH A CLANG.

THE PRIMARY RCS* JETS NUDGE THE ORBITER AWAY FROM THE EMPTY TANK.

*REACTION CONTROL SYSTEM.

EVENTUALLY THE TANK WILL BURN UP AS IT ENTERS THE EARTH'S ATMOSPHERE.

GOOD JOB, PEOPLE.

FLOATING IN WEIGHTLESSNESS, THE CREW CHANGES OUT OF LAUNCH SUITS AND STARTS PREPARING ATLANTIS'S CABIN FOR LIVING IN.

I'M GLAD I TOOK MY ANTINAUSEA PILLS.

FACES PUFF UP AS FLUID, NO LONGER PULLED DOWN BY GRAVITY, MOVES TO HEAD AND CHEST. THE INNER EAR, USED FOR BALANCE, IS ALSO AFFECTED, LEADING TO MOTION SICKNESS.

FLIGHT DAY THREE: ATLANTIS MAKES ITS FINAL APPROACH TO THE ISS.

COCKRELL LEAVES HIS SEAT AND CONTROLS ATLANTIS FROM UNDER THE RIGHT OVERHEAD WINDOW.

90 MINUTES TO DOCKING.

ALPHA, ATLANTIS, HERE WE COME.

TRAVELLING AT EIGHT KILOMETRES PER SECOND, THE SLIGHTEST WRONG MOVE COULD CAUSE DISASTER. (IN 1997, RUSSIA'S MIR SPACE STATION WAS HIT BY A CARGO SPACESHIP, PUNCTURING A HOLE IN MIR'S HULL.)

CAPTURE!

EIGHT FEET, POINT ONE ZERO... SIX FEET POINT ONE...

THE ORBITER SHAKES AS THE DOCKING RINGS SLAM TOGETHER.

MARSHA MAKES THE RANGE CALLS.

ATLANTIS IS SUCCESSFULLY DOCKED WITH THE ISS.

CAPTURE CONFIRMED, HOUSTON.

NICE JOB, EVERYONE.

ROBERT EQUALISES THE PRESSURE IN THE JOINING TUNNEL FROM THE ATLANTIS'S AIRLOCK.

OK, TOM, LET'S SEE HOW YOU DO WITH THIS HATCH.

HA, HA. I SHOULD HAVE SEEN THAT ONE COMING.

ON HIS PREVIOUS MISSION, TOM AND FELLOW ASTRONAUT TAMMY JERNIGAN HAD TO ABORT THEIR FIRST SPACE WALK WHEN THE AIRLOCK HATCH MALFUNCTIONED.

IT'S NOT BUDGING.

THERE IS NO PROBLEM THIS TIME. THE ATLANTIS CREW FLOATS THROUGH TO GREET BILL, YURI AND SERGEI.

WELCOME TO ISS.

AFTER A BRIEF TOUR, THE CREWS RETURN TO ATLANTIS WHERE SEVERAL BAGS OF CARGO ARE HANDED OVER.

FRESH FOOD!

FOUR HOURS AFTER DOCKING, ATLANTIS'S CREW PREPARES FOR THE EVA* THE NEXT DAY. TOM AND ROBERT WEAR MASKS ATTACHED TO PORTABLE OXYGEN BOTTLES TO GET RID OF NITROGEN FROM THEIR BLOOD. THIS WILL STOP THEM FROM GETTING THE BENDS.

*EXTRA-VEHICULAR ACTIVITY.

ON 10 FEBRUARY, ROBERT AND TOM ARE WAITING IN THE AIRLOCK, READY FOR THEIR SPACE WALK. THEY ARE NOW BREATHING PURE OXYGEN TO FLUSH THE LAST OF THE NITROGEN FROM THEIR BLOOD.

CHECKLIST COMPLETE. AIRLOCK DEPRESS VALVE READY.

WHOQOOSH

DEPRESS VALVE TO FIVE.*

*THE AIRLOCK IS DEPRESSURISED TO 5 PSI, TO CHECK THE SUITS FOR ANY LEAKS.

AFTER CHECKING THEIR SUITS, THE ASTRONAUTS VENT THE LAST OF THE AIR OUT OF THE AIRLOCK AND OPEN THE HATCH.

THIS IS IT. MY FIRST SPACE WALK...I HOPE.

THEY UNPLUG THEIR UMBILICALS AND SWITCH ON THEIR SUITS. COOLING WATER, AIR AND ELECTRICITY ARE NOW PROVIDED BY THEIR BACKPACKS.

WOW!

TOM HOOKS HIMSELF AND THEN ROBERT ON TO THEIR 15-METRE SAFETY LINES.

THE ASTRONAUTS QUICKLY START THEIR WORK. THE $1.4-BILLION DESTINY MODULE HAS TO BE INSTALLED WITHIN 36 HOURS, OTHERWISE THE COLD OF SPACE WILL FREEZE THE COOLANT, BURSTING THE HEAT EXCHANGERS.

IF I LET GO, I FEEL I'LL FALL 200 MILES TO EARTH.

OK, BEAMER, WE'RE READY TO GO.

HEH, HEH. IT'S ONLY AN ILLUSION. YOU'LL GET USED TO IT.

IT'S LIKE BALANCING ON A UNICYCLE WHILE TRYING TO SPIN A LUG NUT OFF A WHEEL!

HOW ARE YOU DOING, TOM?

YIKES! THESE BOLTS ARE FROZEN STIFF.

LATER, AS TOM TRIES TO UNDO SOME BOLTS, THE POWER TOOL IS TWISTED OUT OF HIS HANDS. IT TAKES A WHILE TO FREE THE BOLTS.

41

THE VALVES WERE FIXED, AND EVENTUALLY, AFTER SIX HOURS OF EVA, THE ASTRONAUTS WERE READY TO HEAD BACK TO THE AIRLOCK. BEFORE THEY COULD ENTER, THOUGH, TOM HAD TO BRUSH OFF THE AMMONIA FROST-DUST THAT HAD SETTLED ON ROBERT'S SUIT.

AFTER SIX AND A HALF HOURS OF EVA, TOM AND ROBERT MADE IT BACK INSIDE ATLANTIS. DESPITE THE DRAMA, TOM'S FIRST SPACE WALK HAD BEEN A SUCCESS. THE DESTINY LAB WAS POWERED UP AND THE COOLING SYSTEM WORKED, HAVING LOST ONLY FIVE PERCENT OF ITS COOLANT. THE FOLLOWING DAY, THE LAB WAS FITTED OUT AND READY FOR BUSINESS.

TOM AND ROBERT PERFORMED TWO MORE SPACE WALKS, WHICH INCLUDED THE 100TH SPACE WALK BY US ASTRONAUTS. THE MISSION WAS A SUCCESS AND ATLANTIS RETURNED TO EARTH, TOUCHING DOWN IN THE AFTERNOON OF 7 FEBRUARY 2001, 12 DAYS, 21 HOURS AFTER LAUNCH.   **THE END**

HOW TO BECOME AN ASTRONAUT

The European Space Agency (ESA) is always looking for highly qualified, motivated people and accepts applications to train at the European Astronaut Centre (EAC) in Cologne, Germany.

BASIC QUALIFICATIONS

To be an astronaut you will have a high level of education, such as a masters or a doctorate in natural sciences, engineering, information technology or mathematics. You also need to have had at least three years experience in your profession and it helps if you have studied aeronautics and astronautics. To apply as a pilot you must have flown for a minimum of 1000 hours in high performance aircraft. Astronauts need to be in excellent physical condition and will have to undergo intense training which requires strength and endurance. You must be fluent in English and it is also useful to know some Russian for training at the cosmonaut centre in Russia. The preferred age range is 27 to 37. After you fill out an application form and pass the initial selection, you will be sent for psychological testing which takes place in two stages. Following this there are medical tests and an interview before a final decision is made. Basic training lasting one year is followed by another year of advanced training and 18 months increment-specific training for a specific mission.

Astronaut candidates tumble in weightlessness inside a KC-135. They will spend two years training before being selected as an astronaut for a specific mission in space.

GLOSSARY

ammonia A colourless, pungent gas.

antinausea pills Pills that prevent a person from feeling sick.

bends A painful sickness that occurs when nitrogen in the blood expands due to a sudden reduction in air pressure. The bends can be fatal.

cosmonaut A Russian astronaut.

decompression A reduction in air pressure.

deorbit To slow down a spacecraft in orbit so that it falls to Earth.

ejector seat A rocket-propelled seat that carries an astronaut clear of his spacecraft.

g (pronounced jee) G stands for gravity and is short for g-force.

g-force The force a person feels when accelerating. One g is equal to the force acting on a body while standing on Earth.

Kvant 1 module The first addition to the Mir base block which contained scientific instruments for observations and experiments.

multimodular Having many modules.

node Connecting module on a space station.

P6 truss Structure that supports the P6 solar arrays.

quarantine To place a person in an area away from other people so that he or she does not catch an infection.

respirator Self-contained breathing apparatus.

retro rockets Rockets that slow down a spacecraft by firing in the direction of travel.

scrubbers An apparatus that is used for removing impurities from a gas.

simulator A machine with a similar set of controls to the real machine that allows people to train safely.

slurry A runny mixture of solid particles and water.

Spektr module The fifth module of the Mir Space Station. It was designed for remote observation of Earth's environment, and contained atmospheric and surface research equipment.

tethers Safety lines that attach an astronaut to a spacecraft.

umbilicals Tubes that carry oxygen and electricity from a spacecraft to an astronaut's space suit.

unique Unlike anything else.

virtual reality A computer-simulated reality that can be interacted with.

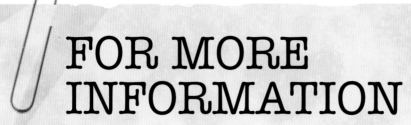

FOR MORE INFORMATION

ORGANISATIONS

ESA Headquarters
8-10 rue Mario Nikis
75738 Paris Cedex 15
France
(0) 33 1 5369 7654
Email: ContactESA@esa.int
Website: http://www.esa.int/esaCP/index.html

John F. Kennedy Space Center
Cape Canaveral, FL 32899
Website: http://www.kennedyspacecenter.com

FOR FURTHER READING

Buckley, James. *Space Heroes: Amazing Astronauts*. London, England: Dorling Kindersley, 2004.

Gilpin, Daniel & Pang, Alex. *Space Vehicles* (Machines Close-Up). London, England: Wayland, 2009.

Jeffrey, Gary. *Incredible Space Missions* (Graphic Discoveries). London, England: Franklin Watts, 2009.

Mitton, Jacqueline. *Moon* (Eyewitness). London, England: Dorling Kindersley, 2009.

Saxton, Curtis. *Star Wars Complete Cross Sections of Spacecraft and Vehicles*. London, England: Dorling Kindersley, 2007.

Stowell, Louie. *Astronomy and Space*. London, England: Usborne Publishing Ltd, 2009.

INDEX